Five Loaves
and Two Fish

KEVIN MAYHEW LTD
Rattlesden Bury St Edmunds
Suffolk England
IP30 0SZ

ISBN 0 86209 361 9

Printed in Great Britain

Five Loaves
and Two Fish

Retold from Scripture by Kathy Singleton
and illustrated by Arthur Baker

Kevin Mayhew

Simon woke up bright and early.
He was so excited. His cousin, Joel,
had come to stay and they were
going fishing. He yawned and
stretched, then jumped onto Joel's
bed. 'Wake up, Jo,' he shouted,
'It's a beautiful day.' Jo rubbed the
sleep from his eyes – then he was
wide awake, too.

'Come and get your breakfast,'
called Simon's Mum. They pulled
on their clothes, and gobbled down
their breakfast. 'Where's our
fishing tackle?' yelled Simon,
hunting around. 'Here you are,'
said his Mum. 'It's with your lunch
basket. There are some barley
loaves and pickled fish. Don't
forget to be back by sunset,'
she called after them as they set off
down the road.

They soon left Bethsaida behind, walking towards Capernaum. Just before the Jordan River Simon shouted to Jo. 'This way!' They turned off the road and slipped

and slithered down a pathway to Simon's favourite fishing spot on the edge of Lake Galilee. There they fished and played and sunned themselves.

Jo was skimming stones across the calm water when he saw a fishing boat. 'Hey, Simon, look!' he called, 'There's a boat coming in.' They scrambled closer and watched as

the men jumped into the water and pulled the boat up the sand. 'They don't seem to have caught any fish,' said Simon. The boys were disappointed.

They decided to go back to their fishing and playing. 'Let's play hide and seek,' said Jo after a while. 'Okay, I'll hide,' said Simon and ran off to a secret place near the roadside. Poor Jo hunted high and low. He just could not find Simon.

Meanwhile, Simon was watching
the people walking along the road.
There seemed to be hundreds of
them all going in the same
direction in a great hurry.
'The Teacher went this way,'
said one; 'I saw his boat land near
here,' said another.

Then Simon noticed a little girl hobbling along on a stick. She sat down on a stone, and a big tear trickled down her cheek.

Simon left his hiding place.
'What's wrong?' he asked her. 'I'm
looking for Jesus,' she sobbed, 'He
sailed across the Lake in a fishing
boat with his friends, but I'm too
tired to go any further.' 'Never
mind,' said Simon. 'I think I know
where he is, and it's not much
further.' Just then, Jo appeared:
'Jo, get our things,' he shouted.
Then the boys carried the little girl
to the place where they had seen
the men and the fishing boat.

17

'There he is!' shouted the little girl, pointing at one of the men from the boat.

By now, many of the other travellers had found Jesus and his disciples, too. So Jesus began talking to the people and telling them wise stories. His disciples were moving among the crowds and bringing the sick to Jesus to be healed. The three children watched in wonder: 'He's so kind and gentle and clever,' they said to each other.

It was getting near suppertime
and the people were hungry.
The children heard Jesus speaking
to Philip, a disciple: 'Where can
we get food for these people?'
'Lord,' said Philip, 'we do not have
the money to buy food for them all.
Send them to the farms and
nearby villages and let them buy
their own food.' 'But they have all
come a long way and are tired,'
said Jesus.

Simon noticed the disciple,
Andrew, standing nearby.
'Please, sir,' Simon said, tugging at
his sleeve, 'we have five loaves
and two fish you can have.'
'That's very kind of you,' said
Andrew, taking Simon to Jesus.
Simon gave the loaves and fish to
Jesus. 'Thank you,' said Jesus,
'this is just what we need,' and he
told the crowd to sit down.

Jesus took the bread, thanked God for providing it, broke it into pieces, and handed it round. Then he did the same with the fish. 'Surely he's not going to feed all these people with just our food?' said Jo.

Sure enough, Jesus did just that! The bread and fish never ran out and others who had brought food began sharing it too.

When everyone had eaten, Jesus told his disciples to collect up the remains. There were twelve baskets full! The children could not believe their eyes! Jesus looked at them and smiled. He had worked a miracle with their food.

But it was late now, and the sun was beginning to set. 'Come on,' said Simon, 'we'd better be going home.' 'Where will you stay?' Jo asked the little girl. 'Don't worry,' said Andrew, we'll take care of her.' They knew she was in good hands as they waved goodbye to their new friends.

Then they turned and ran down
the road back to Bethsaida.
They couldn't wait to tell everyone
about the exciting things they had
seen and heard that day. 'This has
been the best day of my life,'
shouted Jo. 'Mine too,' Simon
shouted back happily.

Note to Parents:
This story can be found according to
the Gospel of John, chapter 6,
verses 1 to 15.